11 8

AXOLOTLS

Endpapers by B. Pengilley. Frontis by Ken Lucas, Steinhart Aquarium.

Acknowledgments

The author would like to acknowledge the assistance given by Dr. F. Billett of Southampton University, Mr. Paul of Keynsham and Dr. R. Thomas of Crawley College. Their help in providing material for the photographs was invaluable, as was the information given by them relating to their different rearing systems.

To Zena,
of whom I ax-a-lotl.

ISBN 0-87666-937-2

Distributed in the UNITED STATES by T.F.H. Publications, Inc., 211 West Sylvania Avenue, Neptune City, NJ 07753; in CANADA by H & L Pet Supplies Inc., 27 Kingston Crescent, Kitchener, Ontario N2B 2T6; Rolf C. Hagen Ltd., 3225 Sartelon Street, Montreal 382 Quebec; in ENGLAND by T.F.H. Publications Limited, 4 Kier Park, Ascot, Berkshire SL5 7DS; in AUSTRALIA AND THE SOUTH PACIFIC by T.F.H. (Australia) Pty. Ltd., Box 149, Brookvale 2100 N.S.W., Australia; in NEW ZEALAND by Ross Haines & Son, Ltd., 18 Monmouth Street, Grey Lynn, Auckland 2 New Zealand; in SINGAPORE AND MALAYSIA by MPH Distributors Pte., 71-77 Stamford Road, Singapore 0617; in the PHILIPPINES by Bio-Research, 5 Lippay Street, San Lorenzo Village, Makati Rizal; in SOUTH AFRICA by Multipet Pty. Ltd., 30 Turners Avenue, Durban 4001. Published by T.F.H. Publications Inc., Ltd. the British Crown Colony of Hong Kong. THIS IS THE 1984 EDITION.

AXOLOTLS

PETER W. SCOTT

Photos by the author unless otherwise acknowledged.

Introducing
the
Axolotl

Because of their plumose gills (1)
and soft bodies, axolotls cannot be
kept with fishes but only in
groups of similar-sized animals (2).

SOME HISTORY

As if the spelling of its name were not enough, the axolotl provides a truly bewildering array of problems. From their introduction into the Jardin des Plantes in the Paris of the nineteenth century, they have held the imagination of scholars and schoolboys alike. Mothers of such enchanted schoolboys are usually less entranced by the grotesque unfinished appearance of these creatures. If the camel can be said to be a horse designed by a committee, then the axolotl really does leave one wondering what they were trying to put together. Its oddities have provided scientists with many intriguing fields of study. (It is a very popular animal in laboratories for the study of larval development and em-

bryology.) In this book I would like to provide some information for the hobbyist or the laboratory technician about the oddities of the axolotl.

One interesting facet of this creature is its name, variously translated as water-slave, water-servant, water-sprite, water-player, water-monstrosity or water-twin. Nahuatl, the language of the Aztecs, is a very complex language. An authority guided Hobart Smith on a search of relevant literature and he came up with a more meaningful translation, water-dog (derived from *atl*, meaning water, and *xolotl*, meaning dog). The exact meaning, if there is one, is lost in the mists of time. It is likely the word had differing connotations depending on the context.

The meanings all relate to Xolotl, an Aztec god with wide responsibilities, including:

the dead and resurrected – in which role he took
   the form of a dog;
games – hence the names water-sprite and
   water-player;
monstrosities such as congenital deformities; and
twins.

A myth relates these different responsibilities. Xolotl, while trying to escape banishment from Earth (death), assumed numerous forms, all grotesquely ugly or paired. He finally assumed the form of the axolotl and was captured, killed and relegated to nourishment of the sun and moon. The axolotl fits both requirements with its grotesque appearance and its double life. The transformation was, it seems, recognized locally even then.

NATIVE USES

The home of the axolotl is in the area to the southeast of Mexico City, where it is indigenous to Lakes Xochimilco and Chalco, which are rich in aquatic life. The lakes are fed by clear springs and were well used by the local population.

Much of Lake Xochimilco is taken up by floating islands of peat entangled with rushes, moss and grass. These islands used to be cultivated by locals. The islands would be anchored using stakes; once they had rooted, they would then have mud from the lake bottom ladled onto them. This resulted in a very fertile "garden" on which flowers, melons, pumpkins and gourds could be grown. The produce would then be sold into Mexico City.

The axolotl and its close relatives have formed a part of the staple diet of natives in Mexico since before the time of the Aztecs. In some local markets axolotls could be bought alive for cooking at home or, like chickens, they would be sold already roasted and ready for eating.

The possibility of setting up farms producing axolotls for the table has been suggested in France, but the suggestions fell on deaf ears for esthetic reasons. Axolotls could be farmed this way in artificial ponds from which fish are excluded. This exclusion of fish would be essential; otherwise the larval axolotls would be eaten by them, since there would be no natural hiding places.

Native recipes for axolotl dishes involve tomato sauce, sweet sauce, chile sauce, as tamales, stuffed tortillas or with squash flowers. The recipes require the axolotls to be boiled, fried, steamed or shredded and seasoned with onion, garlic and chile. The taste is reported to be similar to that of eels. The animals are prepared for cooking by evisceration, decapitation, skinning and mashing.

It is perhaps not unexpected that natives have found medicinal uses for axolotls. They are reported to be particularly nourishing to people suffering from chronic diseases such as consumption. This was so widely believed that an axolotl syrup was marketed particularly for respiratory infections, including tuberculosis. These properties have not been properly assessed by medical experts, so the medicinal worth of axolotls remains uncertain.

In nature the dark colored axolotl predominates. It may

Adult tiger salamander, *Ambystoma tigrinum tigrinum,* of the eastern subspecies. Photo by H. Hansen, Aquarium Berlin.

A typical gilled axolotl.

Sixteenth century Aztec jade statue of Xolotl, who is shown as a skeletal creature from the land of the dead.

Ambystoma (Bathysiredon) dumerilii, a close relative of the axolotl. Photo by Dr. S.A. Minton.

Map of Mexico showing the range of *Ambystoma mexicanum*, the axolotl.

Although larval tiger salamenders have gills (1), these are soon lost in normal development. Several other salamanders, however, have gills throughout life. These include the sirens, such as *Siren intermedia* (2), and hellbenders, such as *Cryptobranchus alleganiensis* (3). Photo (1) by R. Zukal, others by Dr. S.A. Minton.

2

3

2

A comparison of a gilled axolotl (1) with tiger salamander larvae (2, 3) shows many similarities and few obvious differences. Photo 1 by M.F. Roberts, others by R. Zukal.

3

In the laboratory, axolotls can be held in a variety of containers, from aquaria to plastic shoe boxes. Equipment like that used to raise trout eggs, a trough with a series of steel baskets through which debris can fall, is also used.

The axolotl tank can form a part of the aquarist's display.
The tank situated above the books contains several axolotls
and is complete with an undergravel filter operating off the
same pump that operates the other two tanks.

1

2

Three subspecies of tiger salamander, *Ambystoma tigrinum:* 1) *A. t. melanostictum;* 2) *A. t. mavortium;* 3) *A. t. californiense.* Photos 1 and 3 by Ken Lucas, Steinhart Aquarium; photo 2 by F.H. Pough, Jr.

3

1

1) Young axolotls can be safely kept in groups if well fed, but some floating plants should be added to provide shelter. 2) A male axolotl from above. 3) A female axolotl from above; notice the more rounded abdomen due to the presence of eggs and the somewhat shorter and broader head than that of the male.

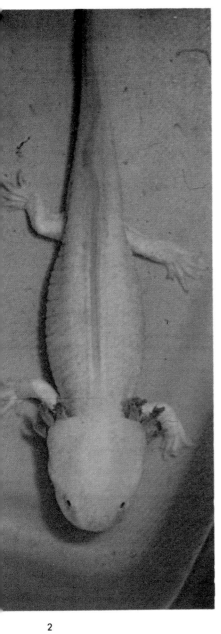

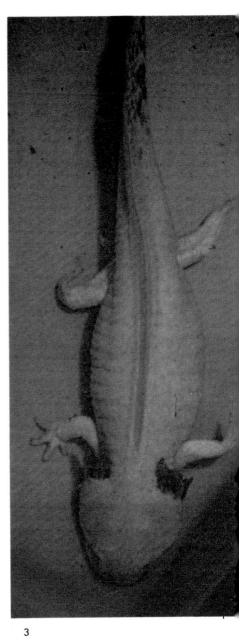

2

3

vary from black or dark olive green to dark brown skin with black spots and diffuse gray-brown patches. Occasionally even light green animals may be seen. Details of inheritance of color patterns and some variations on this basic pattern are discussed later in the section on genetics.

CLASSIFICATION

We should start trying to follow the trail of confusion with a description of where the axolotl fits into the overall classification of animals.

The axolotl is an amphibian, a term derived from the Greek—*amphi* meaning double and *bios* meaning life. This suggests a double life, part in water and part on land. The axolotl manages to confound even this basic definition by its "preference" for remaining in the water as a sexually mature larva.

It belongs to the order of amphibians known as Caudata or Urodela. This group is so called because they retain their tails into adult life. Aquarists know these animals as the newts and salamanders.

To narrow down the classification still further, the axolotl belongs to the genus *Ambystoma*. The term axolotl should be restricted to the species *Ambystoma mexicanum* from Lake Xochimilco and Lake Chalco. It has also been used to describe the larval form of the tiger salamander (*Ambystoma tigrinum*) which exists as various subspecies throughout most of the United States of America except the high Appalachians, the far Southwest and southern Florida.

The gilled axolotl was originally named *Siredon mexicanum* and the adult salamander form was called *Ambystoma mexicanum*. To rationalize the situation, herpetologist Hobart M. Smith suggested that the generic name *Siredon* be restricted to two Mexican species which rarely transform into adult salamanders, *i.e.*, *Siredon mexicanum* and *Siredon dumerilii*. The latter species has extensive webbing between the digits, which differentiates it from *S. mexicanum* and *A. tigrinum*. It is found in Lake Patzcuaro, Michoacán. He further suggested that the genus *Ambystoma* be limited to the numerous forms which metamorphose regularly, such as the tiger salamander, *A. tigrinum,* and the very different looking *A. altamirani,* which is found in mountain streams to the west of Mexico City. This latter species has collected some intriguing names locally, including *axolotes sin aletas,* without winglets (gills); *axolotes del cerro,* mountain axolotl; and *axolotes sordos,* deaf axolotl (no ears?). Other species found in the area of Mexico City are *A. lacustris* from Lake Zumpango and *A. lermaensis* from Lake Lerma. As larvae, these are virtually identical in color and pattern to *A. mexicanum.*

There are strong arguments against Hobart Smith's classification. The axolotl is no doubt very closely related to species of *Ambystoma* and should be included in this genus. They have been successfully interbred. One solution which makes some sense is to call the rare metamorphosed axolotl *Ambystoma* and the neotenic form *Siredon,* but taxonomists and herpetologists in general are unlikely to accept such a "double standard."

The tiger salamander has already been mentioned. It has been suggested that it was this species (that in some areas associated with low iodine levels remains as a larva) which gave rise to the Mexican species. Of the dozen or more endemic Mexican ambystomids, three similar species, *A. mexicanum, A. altamirani* and *A. dumerilii,* all inhabit the old drainage system of the Lerma River, an area noted for its peculiar fish species. This suggests a long period of isolation from other freshwater fish. The suggestion is that *A. tigrinum* was widely distributed across Mexico but that the Lerma system became isolated by lava flows and the three forms also became isolated, developing along separate lines.

Biology and Anatomy

Whether brown (1) or white (2), axolotls present the same general appearance until they metamorphose. Photo 1 by Dr. S.A. Minton.

BIOLOGY

The key to the fascination of the axolotl is its Peter Pan-like ability to avoid growing up. It is one of the amphibian species exhibiting "neoteny," which means that it can live out its life and successfully breed as a larva.

Almost all of the urodeles develop from eggs through a larval tadpole-like stage with gills and a tail. They gradually grow legs and eventually metamorphose into adults, losing their gills. The axolotl, along with a number of other species, has the ability to remain as a larva, and indeed this is its normal state. The potential for metamorphosis under appropriate environmental conditions seems to be determined genetically. Some strains of axolotl metamorphose

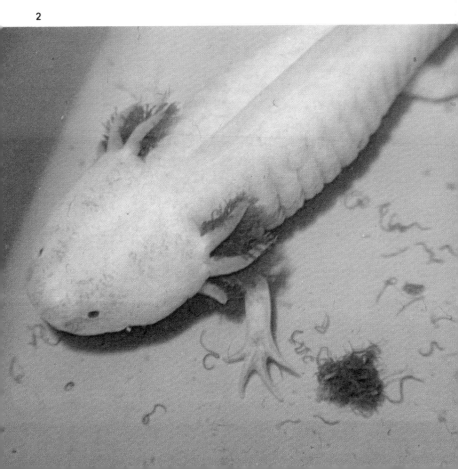

readily while others are very reluctant or totally unable to do so. The axolotls first seen in Europe at the Jardin des Plantes caused a considerable stir. There had been uncertainty as to where to place these creatures in the classification of amphibians. In 1865 a bombshell dropped—one of the broods of larvae which the keepers had successfully bred showed some individuals with a slightly different coloration. Nothing was thought odd, however, until these larvae grew into mature axolotls, lost their gills and turned into salamanders. (Oddly enough, the Jardin des Plantes stock seems to be of the type which rarely metamorphoses.)

We should dwell for a while on the subjects of neoteny and metamorphosis. Neoteny is considered as being a prime factor in evolution. The earliest vertebrates are thought to have evolved from neotenic sea squirts; and, nearer to home, similarities have been pointed out between the adult human and the embryonic or juvenile ape. Among the amphibians neoteny represents a "backward step" since it prevents colonization of the land.

It is interesting to speculate why neoteny has become so prevalent in the species. It is certainly now inherited. Some strains remain neotenic as long as they are inbred, but if crossed with a metamorphosing race they will produce metamorphosing offspring. The obvious mechanism is survival of the fittest. This, however, presupposes that there is an advantage in remaining as a sexually precocious larva, such as unfavorable conditions on land and advantageous conditions in the water. There is one advantage to be seen: since these species live at high altitudes and have a late breeding season, their survival is likely to be much better if they can remain in the water over the winter. It is possible that the first step toward neoteny was a late metamorphosing strain.

Another factor to be considered is light. The amphibian pituitary (a gland attached to the brain) requires the stimulus of light to make it secrete a thyroid-stimulating hormone. This is thought to be a major factor in the evolution of some of the neotenic cave dwellers. Although a deficiency in light is unlikely at high altitudes, it may well be that larvae living under the ice in ponds may settle in darker areas and be deprived of light through the winter. This depression of the pituitary may not always recover and may over a great many generations lead to the assimilation into the genetic make-up of a character that was originally environmental.

Finally, any individuals capable of breeding as larvae are likely to begin to outnumber others simply by virtue of a shorter generation interval. This whole subject is one fraught with speculation; but whatever the answer is, it is likely to be a multifactorial one, possibly a combination of all the ideas already mentioned plus a few others.

The physiological mechanism which controls metamorphosis is a little uncertain. It is believed to involve the thyroid gland and its hormone thyroxine (T4). Thyroxine stimulates metabolism in the tissue generally, including promoting growth and development. Thyroxine release is regulated by the thyrotrophic hormone (T.S.H.) from the anterior pituitary gland, which in turn is regulated by thyrotrophin-releasing factor (T.R.F.) from an area of the brain called the hypothalamus. It is thought that in the axolotl activity in this T.R.F.-T.S.H.-T4 axis is low, primarily at the level of the hypothalamus. There is much speculation regarding whether external or internal factors responsible for activating this axis are lacking or whether, for genetic or other reasons, some strains are insensitive to them.

There are a few other species whose adults remain in the larval state. Many of these hide away in underwater vegetation, pond bottoms or the cool waters of deep caverns. These include: the hellbenders *(Cryptobranchus)* from the cold streams and lakes of the eastern United States, China and Japan; the so-called Congo eels or amphiumas *(Am-*

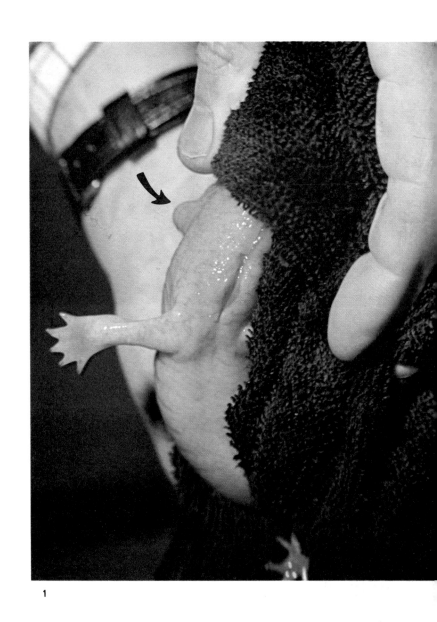

1

Close-ups of the cloacal regions of
male (1) and female (2) axolotls.
The cloaca of the male is considerably more swollen than that
of the female.

30

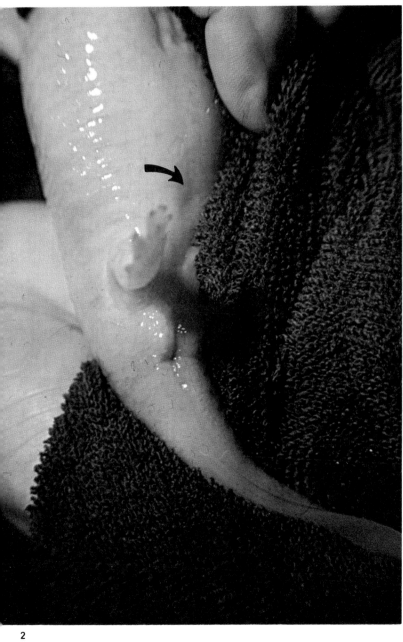

Other examples of primitive gilled
salamanders. 1) *Andrias david-
ianus,* the giant salamander of
China. Photo by Ken Lucas,
Steinhart Aquarium. 2) *Amphiuma
means,* a congo-eel. Photo by F.J.
Dodd, Jr. 3) Head of *Siren lacer-
tina.* Photo by Ken Lucas,
Steinhart Aquarium.

phiuma) from the southeastern United States; the sirens *(Siren)* of the southern United States; and the mudpuppies *(Necturus)* of the eastern United States. The species living in caves include the European olm *(Proteus anguineus)* from caves in Yugoslavia and several unrelated species from the United States, including *Typhlomolge, Haideotriton* and species of *Gyrinophilus*.

Supposedly there is a link between the distribution of some of these species and iodine-deficient regions. Iodine is an integral part of thyroid hormones and if deficient in supply leads to thyroid depression. This may have been a part of the evolutionary pressure involved in the development of neoteny, but it has now become an integral part of the genotype of some species, such that if supplied with iodine, subjected to environmental stress or even directly injected with thyroid hormones they will not metamorphose.

From what has been said so far on the subject, it may be surmised that induction of metamorphosis is not the simple procedure that many herpetologists assume. Traditional methods, *i.e.,* gradually lowering the water level or putting the axolotl in damp moss rather than water, have always resulted in high death rates. Similarly, the more scientific method of injecting iodine compounds or thyroid hormones has met with some failures. The reason is clear — some strains have completely lost the ability to metamorphose and will die if forced out of the water.

It is worth looking at what metamorphosis involves. It is a series of changes undergone by the various organs of the body marking the transition from the aquatic life to the terrestrial life. It radically alters the outward appearance. The first signs are a narrowing of the head. As it becomes more pointed, the eyes begin to protrude; the fin along the back and tail folds over and fuses with the skin of the back, which thickens. The gills shrink and finally vanish. At the same time the lungs become enlarged to provide more oxygen for the animal's new life on land.

1

The mudpuppy *(Necturus)* (1) is the most familiar and common gilled adult salamander and is probably one of the most primitive salamanders. Photo by Ken Lucas, Steinhart Aquarium. At the other extreme is the highly specialized cave-dwelling *Haideotriton wallacei*, which also retains gills into adulthood (2). Photo by F.J. Dodd, Jr.

2

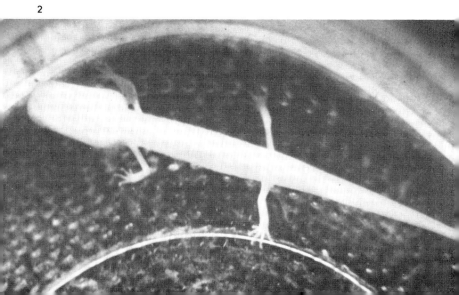

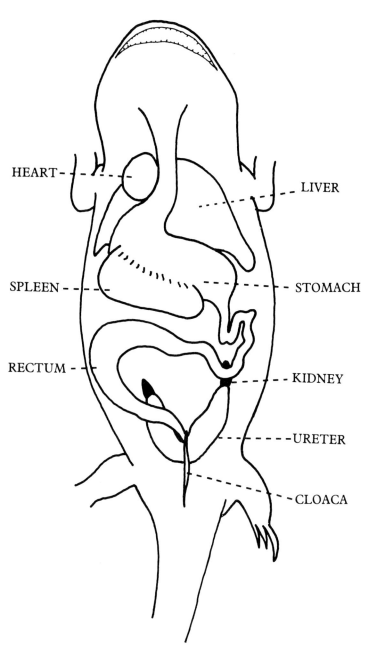

HEART

LIVER

SPLEEN

STOMACH

RECTUM

KIDNEY

URETER

CLOACA

Internal anatomy of the axolotl.

The life span of axolotls once metamorphosed is said to be reduced. The larval form is known to regularly survive 10-12 years, and a specimen kept at Covent Garden in London is reported to have lived 25 years. One might expect that with a higher level of thyroid activity metamorphosed axolotls would have a higher metabolic rate and subsequently shorter lifespans. The regenerative capacity from wounds is also reduced after metamorphosis and is unlikely to occur at all—normal healing is more likely to occur.

ANATOMY

Just like any other vertebrate, the body of an axolotl is built around a skeleton. The basic plan is vaguely the same as our own, though differing in numerous details and in the fact that even in old axolotls it isn't completely bony. In particular the wrists, ankles and supporting apparatus of the gills are still composed of cartilage. The number of vertebrae varies (the average is 50) due mainly to the tail region, which usually has 30-35 vertebrae. One interesting feature is the presence of rudimentary ribs on the thoracic vertebrae.

On the skeletal framework is a powerful musculature. Segmental muscle blocks similar to those of fishes comprise most of the body. These enable the axolotl to move sinuously through the water in a movement different from that of a land animal. In fact, in metamorphosis the ventral portion of the muscles becomes thinner, since the even wriggling of the body is not required for locomotion any longer. The limbs are controlled by specialized muscle groups just as they would be in a dog or a cat.

Internally the axolotl is again similar to any other animal in principle. Some of the details differ, but the basic pattern is not changed much. Food is taken in by the large gaping mouth—a feature responsible for the scientific name *Ambystoma (i.e., Ambyx* meaning cup and *stoma* meaning mouth). The function of the mouth is to grip, since the axolotl doesn't chew its food but bolts it in stages. To this end the mouth is equipped with fine teeth on both upper and lower jaws. In the mouth is a thick fixed tongue similar to that found in fishes. The mouth can give a powerful bite, but it is unlikely to do any harm since the teeth are barely noticeable.

Food passes through the short esophagus to the stomach. Digestion occurs in the stomach and intestine. Digestion may well be aided by the multiple punctures caused by the many teeth in the surfaceof any prey, so that digestive enzymes can enter through these fine punctures. The intestine is short, as is typical of a carnivore. The lower end of the intestine is expanded and forms the cloaca (from the Latin for a sewer); the cloaca receives both intestinal waste and urinary waste.

The urinary system differs from mammals. There are two small kidneys leading into large sac-like ureters and finally a small bladder. Excretion in axolotls also involves the gills. The larval axolotl excretes 50% of its nitrogenous waste as ammonia, and much of this is lost via the gills. The rest of the ammonia and the urea, which is the other nitrogenous waste product, are lost through the kidneys in the copious, highly diluted urine. The urine is very dilute because water is constantly entering the animal by osmosis (salts are present in its body at a higher concentration than the surrounding water).

When axolotls metamorphose, the balance changes and only 25% of the nitrogenous waste is excreted as ammonia. This is because with the animal living on land, water becomes precious and ammonia is more toxic than urea when concentrated, so the safer compound of the two is excreted.

The main function of the gills is respiration. Young axolotls with their relatively large feathery gills obtain the oxygen they need through the gills and through the skin. Gas exchange through the skin is important in amphibians in general. They have a moist skin with a generous blood supply and can take in a good deal of their oxygen requirements this way. The oxygen requirements of young axolotls are relatively great. They have a rapid growth rate and are fairly active due to their search for food. As they grow, their metabolism slows and they become less active. Large axolotls supplement their oxygen by also filling their rudimentary lungs at the surface. They can be seen to periodically rise to the surface and gulp.

The lungs of the neotenic axolotl are very small and simple; they are basically a cavity with a honeycomb-like pattern to the walls. These lungs develop and become more important when the axolotl loses its gills in metamorphosis. The metamorphosed animal probably obtains more oxygen through the skin than does the neotenic form, due to the fact that air contains more oxygen than water. In fact, some small salamanders have no lungs and need to rely solely on skin absorption (cutaneous respiration).

The detailed structure of the gills varies a good deal. Some animals have a very exuberant growth while others have a very scanty display of filaments. There are probably several reasons for this. There are supposed to be genetic factors leading to stunted or reduced gill development, but there is little doubt that environment also plays a part. Exuberant plumose gills are not required for old animals or animals restrained in small containers with adequate oxygen. In time gills seem to atrophy and the animals obtain most of their requirement for oxygen through the lungs and by cutaneous respiration.

The anatomy of axolotls is subject to variation for a very unusual reason. Any portions of the animal bitten off or seriously damaged are likely to be regenerated. Limbs, portions of the tail, gills and even part of the head will usually regenerate. The undamaged axolotl has four toes on the front feet and five toes on the back feet. In practice, due to this property of regeneration after injuries, the actual

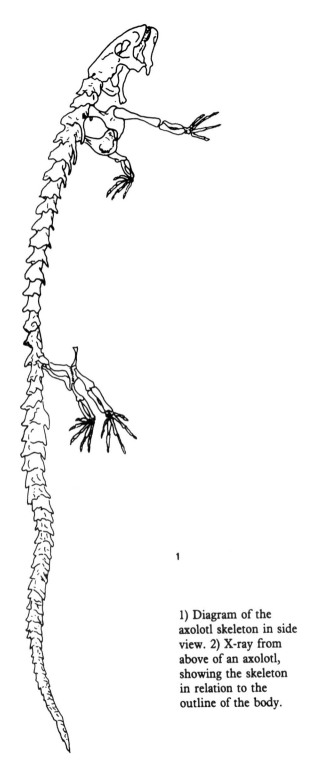

1) Diagram of the axolotl skeleton in side view. 2) X-ray from above of an axolotl, showing the skeleton in relation to the outline of the body.

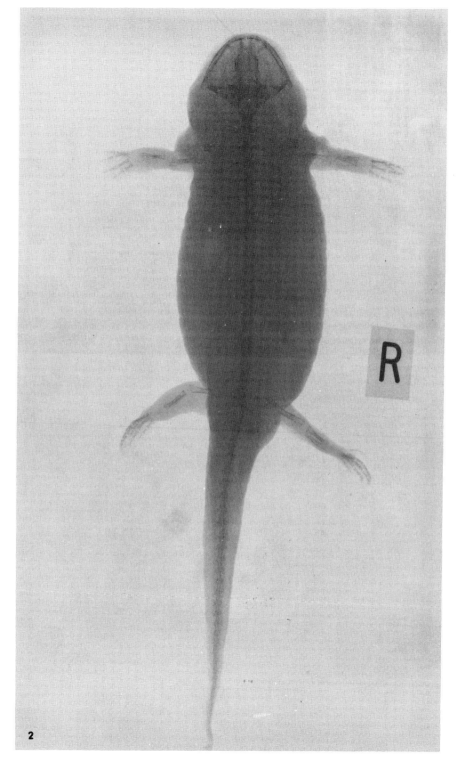

2

number varies from zero to six toes on each foot. Occasionally partial loss of a limb may result in a new limb growing alongside the healing original limb. Complete regeneration of a limb in a young axolotl normally takes two or three months, but this is appreciably slower in adults. Once the animals have metamorphosed, healing is very much reduced and regeneration of lost portions is unlikely to occur.

The regeneration of organs such as the liver, spleen and eye is reported after partial removal from larvae. For obvious reasons any animal suffering from this type of damage has a very poor outlook and a slim chance of survival.

Considering that the axolotl is poikilothermic (cold-blooded) and that its metabolic processes are dependent on temperature—being rapid at higher temperatures and vice versa—it is a curious observation that healing and regeneration seem to be more rapid at lower temperatures. This is contrary to the healing of wounds in fishes, where the rate of healing is almost directly dependent on temperature.

As mentioned earlier, the regenerative ability of axolotls once they have undergone metamorphosis is very much reduced. If they suffer damage it is more likely to be repaired in a more conventional manner.

Facing page: Metamorphosis radically alters the appearance of the axolotl. The gills disappear, the head becomes narrower, the eyes become protuberant, and the dorsal fin fuses to the skin of the back.

1

Care of Axolotls

1) Most axolotls can be taught to take food from forceps or the fingers. 2) Once metamorphosed, axolotls can be kept in vivaria with low water levels.

HOUSING

The first consideration of the axolotl owner should be where he is going to keep it. Axolotls don't require running water or specially aerated water. Provided the container used has adequate surface area and is kept clean, then nothing special is required. A variety of containers may be used. Laboratories may use aquaria or the now outdated globe fish bowls. Rectangular plastic containers are popular as they are easily stacked and stored, and even one-gallon plastic shoeboxes have been used. There is also a unit designed for holding aquatic amphibians which consists of a series of perforated baskets hanging in a metal trough. This unit is based on a filtered recirculation system to make cleaning easier.

2

The needs of the pet keeper who wants to see his pet are different from those of the laboratory technician who is more interested in the mass production of the animals. The average pet keeper will want to use an aquarium that can be readily fitted into the aquarist's set-up. A depth of water of approximately 25 cm is advisable, and a 50 x 100 cm tank gives the animals plenty of room to swim. Six axolotls could be held comfortably in such a tank. Smaller tanks may also be used, but the animals are often noticeably less active.

Water chemistry seems relatively unimportant. A pH range of 6.5 to 8.5 has been found to suit most amphibians, and the lower end of this range is the ideal. Problems are reported with axolotls at pH 4, which is not altogether unexpected since such water would be considered hostile by many fishes also.

Water quality is important. Normal aquarium filters are adequate when combined with routine use of an aquarium vacuum cleaner. Undergravel filters drawing water and wastes through the gravel, using this as a filter bed, do a good job. The solid wastes of the axolotl, however, will not be drawn through adequately, so routine vacuum cleaning of the tank bottom after feeding is a worthwhile precaution to maintain water quality. Again, box filters and even certain power filters may not pick up some of the larger solid wastes and uneaten food, thus requiring a routine clean-up.

One other factor which should be stressed is that since the undergravel filter is based on the action of a bacterial growth in the gravel bed, the pump drawing oxygenated water through it must not be turned off, otherwise the bacteria will die and the filtered material will ferment, releasing toxic compounds. The system now popular with aquarists keeping marine fishes would probably be the method of choice, a power filter used to push water in the reversed direction through an undergravel filter. This means any particulate matter is washed out of the gravel and picked up by the filter. The alternative to filtration is a routine total water change. With filtration a 1/10th water change weekly will suffice. Tapwater is suitable for axolotls, but it should be left to stand for 24 hours to lose chlorine or else a proprietary aquarium dechlorinator should be used.

When setting up the tank, it is natural to want to make it an attractive setting for the axolotls. Large gravel can be used together with rocks to provide places to stand and other hiding places. Any plants used should be robust and well rooted, otherwise they will surely be uprooted by the axolotls blundering through them. Plants such as *Cerato-phyllum* are suitable. From the standpoint of ease of cleaning and maintenance, good quality plastic plants are probably the ideal choice.

It is unnecessary to use special lights for the aquarium—normal room lighting is adequate except when it is desired to view the animals. Normal daylight of some 10-12 hours each day is sufficient, although some shelter should be provided so that the animals can retire in seclusion for a time. This is particularly important if the tank is situated in brightly lit surroundings. The reason for this is that axolotls are to a large extent nocturnal. They are certainly more active in dim light and have no eyelids to protect them from harsh lighting.

The optimum temperature is 14-18°C; below 10°C they become dull and refuse to eat. At certain times, although the water temperature may be high enough during the day for them to accept food, it may drop at night. This will often cause regurgitation of a pellet of food, which may happen even two days after eating.

Axolotls should be handled gently. A large net may be used to trap them initially, but they should then be grasped firmly but gently with one hand around the neck and shoulders, thus restraining the forelegs and head, and the other hand around the lower abdomen, hind legs and base

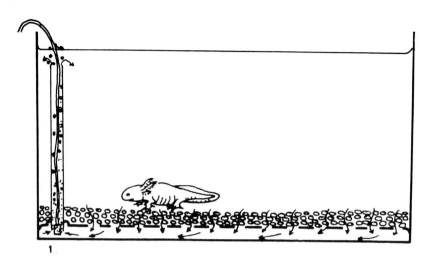

Diagrams of water flow in a normal undergravel filter (1) and a reverse-flow filter (2). Whatever type of filter is used, however, the large pieces of debris and feces will have to be siphoned off individually.

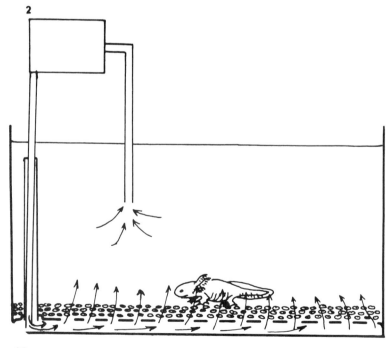

Three common types of filters. 1) A modern corner filter. 2) A power filter. 3) A sponge filter, actually a type of corner filter using a special sponge to increase the area of absorption.

2

1

3

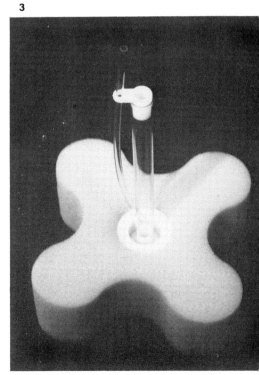

49

of the tail. Excessive use of the net is best avoided, otherwise the legs may become tangled and damaged. Also, an axolotl will beat its tail vigorously when restrained and may damage it considerably. When using the hands, avoid squeezing the axolotl, remembering that the bones are cartilaginous and fairly soft. Also avoid damaging the gills.

When nets are used, the shallow ones are preferred or even a home-made net with a piece of nylon fabric stretched across a square of iron wire.

FEEDING

In nature the adult axolotl feeds on a variety of small aquatic creatures including worms, insects, crustaceans and small fishes. In the laboratory or the herpetologist's home such a varied diet is rarely available. Adult axolotls seem to thrive on a diet of raw beef liver; pig liver should be avoided as this seems to cause regurgitation. Good quality beef meat can also be used, the fat and tendon being trimmed off first since these are very poorly digested. Beef or lamb heart is an economical and suitable food. The simplest way of preparing food is to cut it into strips up to 0.5 cm across and 3 to 4 cm long. (Pieces that are too large may be regurgitated.) The prepared strips can then be wrapped in meal-sized portions and deep-frozen. The amount that can be eaten at one meal varies with the size of the animal, its stage of maturity and the temperature of the water.

Digestion occurs slowly, taking two or three days to digest a meal on the average. This is more rapid at high temperatures and slower if temperatures are low. Regurgitation if the temperature falls below 10°C has been mentioned. This is probably a safety mechanism to avoid food souring in the intestine due to the slower passage or even total stoppage at low temperatures. If this occurred, the animal might be poisoned by any toxins released from the decomposing food.

Axolotls should be fed two or three times weekly, again dependent on temperature. Animals to be bred should be particularly well fed—they may even eat daily just before they are ready to breed. This is necessary for them to produce eggs or sperm of adequate quality.

Some axolotls will feed from a container in their tank. This tends to cause excess food to be spread over the whole tank. It is preferable for pet axolotls, at least, to be hand-fed. If mainly heart is fed, it is worthwhile supplementing with both fat-soluble and water-soluble vitamins. Some laboratories feed minced meat and multivitamins in a container placed on the bottom. If this type of feeding is practiced, then any fecal matter should be siphoned out first, otherwise it is stirred up by bottom feeding and unhygienic conditions develop. Another common laboratory regime is the provision of tubifex worms so they are constantly available in the otherwise bare tank. The salamanders are then hand-fed once a week, increasing to daily feedings before breeding.

A certain amount of live food such as tadpoles and earthworms may be provided. However, for reasons of disease avoidance, foods of aquatic origin are best given with great caution. The small red earthworms from a compost heap are greatly appreciated by axolotls, and, provided care is taken to collect them where no dangerous chemicals or fertilizers are used, they should be safe enough.

The technique of hand-feeding is simply to move a strip of meat in front of the axolotl, which will usually snap vigorously at it with a surprising burst of speed. The use of forceps is probably best, although some people prefer to use their fingers.

In recent years packets of freeze-dried and deep-frozen irradiated foods have become commercially available. These are popular with many aquarists since they provide a ready method of varying the diet. Used this way they are admirable, but certain of these foods may be unsuitable as sole diets for axolotls due to their high oil content and may lead to liver problems.

The feeding of axolotls is a subject requiring some more scientific investigation—there are many variations on a basic theme. A number of people find that their axolotls eat a certain amount of vegetable matter. This may occur in the wild, but the structure of the digestive system would suggest that such food probably is digested poorly. The mouth is essentially a grasping and tearing organ that is not equipped for grinding up plant material, nor is the intestine equipped for holding large volumes of vegetable matter.

Trout pellets are used by some people. These are formulated to the needs of the trout, a basically carnivorous fish which in the wild eats a diet similar to that of the axolotl. Axolotls need to be trained to accept these as food, but once this is accomplished they should provide an adequate diet. One problem with feeding trout pellets is the eventual disintegration of uneaten pellets. Feeding should be carefully monitored to avoid this. Such pellets are available as floating or sinking formulations—the former are likely to retain their shape longer. The present use of a fat coating on some of these pellets will also help. If these pellets are not available, it is simple enough to coat pellets at home using commercially available gelatin or agar-agar.

A common finding among laboratories and individual pet owners is that their pets are more active at night. The axolotl may have developed this more nocturnal existence to protect it from predators. They certainly seem more willing to feed in the late evening and are more active in their tanks. Spawning activity also seems to take place primarily in the dark.

The nocturnal habit may cause problems if food is presented only during the day. The animals may feed very little and become so weak they cannot feed. In other cases the axolotls looking for food at night may attack their fellows and bite off limbs and gills. This is particularly important with larval axolotls, which must be well fed; otherwise they may attack each other.

1

1) Tubifex worms are a controversial food for axolotls. They are readily accepted but might cause digestive problems. Photo by Dr. H.R. Axelrod. 2) Hold an axolotl with both hands, one behind the head and the other about the hind legs.

2

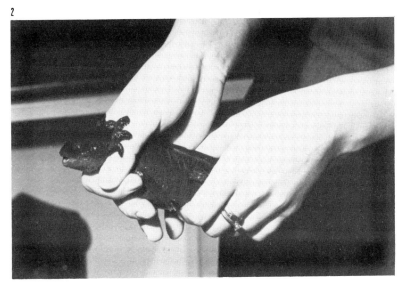

53

Many axolotls adapt well to hand-feeding. The food can be presented with the fingers, but a pair of forceps is usually more practical. The teeth of axolotls are very fine, and it is unlikely accidents will happen even if you use your fingers. By hand-feeding you are likely to notice if any animals are not eating.

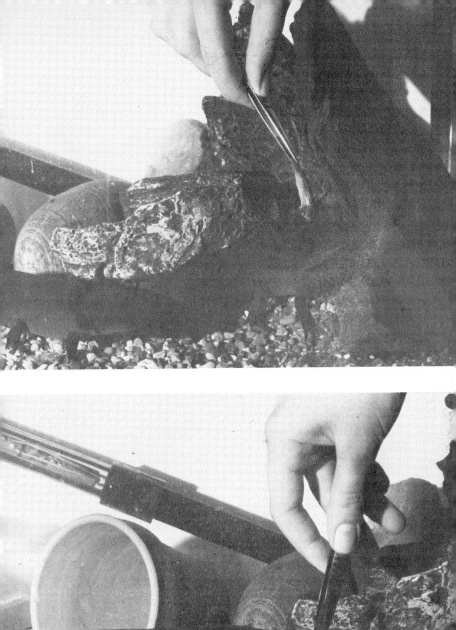

Live foods such as tadpoles (1) and earthworms (2) are accepted by most axolotls if they are the proper size. Such food can transfer parasites, however. Photo above courtesy American Museum of Natural History, that below by P. Imgrund.

Living plants such as elodea are valuable in the axolotl tank for many reasons, such as protection of young and weak adults, shade from excessive light, and as an attractive background for the admittedly unspectacular colors of the salamanders.

Cannibalism among axolotl larvae does not seem to occur if they are kept in green water or in a heavily planted aquarium with reduced light. For the laboratory or serious axolotl breeder, one method of simulating these conditions is the use of special netting made to reduce the passage of light. Once axolotls have reached a length of about 10 cm they are past this cannibalistic phase and can be kept in normal light conditions.

The feeding of young axolotl larvae is a special technique and will be mentioned later in the section dealing with breeding.

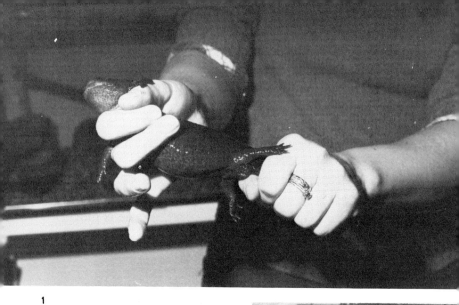

1

1) Female axolotls ready for spawning have obviously enlarged abdomens. 2) If elodea or other plants are provided in the spawning tank, the eggs can be removed for incubation.

Breeding Axolotls

Sexual maturity in axolotls is reached at around 12 months of age. This is marked in the male by an increase in the size of the cloacal glands, producing swelling of the margins of the cloaca.

Differentiating the sexes is not possible until the sex characteristics develop, so juvenile animals cannot be sexed accurately. Sexing is difficult and sometimes impossible with single specimens – the best way is by comparing adults. Features to look for are: 1) the cloaca is larger and has more swollen margins in the male; 2) the male is more

slender with a longer tail; and 3) the head of the male is narrower and longer than that of the female.

Ideally axolotls should be left until two years old before breeding. This allows them time to reach a suitable size and condition. In the female a rounded body contour develops as eggs are produced. There is a slight enlargement of the female cloaca as she reaches sexual maturity, but it is not as marked as that of the male.

The natural breeding season, from December to June, is probably controlled by a combination of photoperiod (day length) and water temperature. This isn't inviolable, however, as young animals reaching maturity in spring may produce eggs outside this period. Under artificial conditions the most successful time for breeding is the latter portion of the natural season, *i.e.,* March to June.

It is not enough to put male and female together. It is necessary to create conditions which will stimulate breeding. This usually involves an environmental change, normally a change in temperature. It does not seem critical whether this change is upward or downward, merely that a constant temperature be established for some weeks before the sudden change is imposed.

Perhaps the best and most reliable method of spawning is to raise the water temperature in the holding tank to about 22°C for one week, then transfer a male and female into a spawning tank at a temperature of 12°C. The spawning tank should be furnished with a mass of elodea for eggs to be deposited on, and flat slates or plates should be placed on the bottom for spermatophore deposition.

Fertilization is internal but is achieved by indirect means. The male swims around and deposits small packets of sperm enclosed in a cone of mucus. This mucus is produced in the cloacal glands of the male axolotl and accounts for the swelling of these glands in the mature male animal.

There is a mating ritual. It begins with the male swimming around the female, elevating his tail and making

60

writhing movements. He leads the female around, often scraping his cloaca on the substratum, depositing a spermatophore and then leading the female over it. At this time the female shows a great deal of interest in the cloaca of the male, continually nudging it with her snout. The male also shows an interest in the cloaca of the female, and there may well be some snout-to-vent "waltzing" around the tank prior to spermatophore deposition. Up to 25 spermatophores may be deposited in one night by the male. Several of these may be picked up by the female. Egg laying (oviposition) takes place approximately 24 hours later. During all this activity the axolotls are usually more settled if they are left where they are less likely to be disturbed. Even so, most of the spawning activity will take place at night.

There may be from 300 to 1100 eggs in one spawning. Each egg has a gelatinous coat which helps it to stick to surfaces in the tank. This coating swells dramatically on contact with the water, causing a doubling in the overall size of the egg within a few hours.

If a mass of elodea has been provided, then the eggs will probably be laid on it. The mass can then be removed to another tank containing aged water and equipped with an aerator. This is preferred since the pair of axolotls may spawn again later in the season and might be put off by moving them to another tank.

Eggs attached to plants develop much better than eggs collected from the bottom of the tank, presumably because the former receive more oxygen. Adequate aeration is essential for successful development of eggs. The method used in many laboratories—placing a layer of eggs in a shallow dish and relying on oxygenation at the surface—is prone to problems.

Overcrowding results in deaths and abnormal development of many of the survivors. The reason for this is that eggs are the fastest developing stage in the life cycle of the axolotl, and they have the highest metabolic rate, weight for weight. Consequently they have the highest demand for oxygen and the highest output of waste products. If the eggs are overcrowded, then the lack of oxygen can kill them or the metabolic wastes can cause malformations or even deaths if the buildup is severe enough.

The rate of development of the eggs is dependent on environmental temperature, but two weeks to hatching is about the average. Living embryos often will be seen moving inside the gelatinous coats of the eggs. While eggs are developing they should be protected from direct sunlight and sudden temperature changes; the optimum temperature range for rearing eggs is 14-18°C.

Dead eggs and embryos are easily distinguished from the living eggs by their light grayish color and lack of activity within them. These dead eggs can be a threat if the water conditions are poor, as they provide a focus for fungal infestations such as saprolegnia, which begins on dead eggs and spreads to adjoining live ones. For this reason any dead or diseased eggs should be removed as soon as possible.

Since it is the gelatinous coat which provides the site for growth of bacteria and fungi, a technique used in some laboratories is to gently separate the outer, softer jelly from the deeper, firmer layer with a blunt knife. These dehusked eggs may then be dipped in 70% ethanol for about 10 seconds for partial sterilization of their surfaces.

As the embryo develops in the egg, the larva takes shape. It leaves the egg with small feathery gills and a long tail. Two rods of tissue growing out from the sides of the head are called balancers and have a sticky glandular area on the ends. These enable the larva to anchor itself to the substrate. As the axolotl grows its gills enlarge, and after a couple of weeks the forelimbs develop. After a further two to three weeks the hind limbs then develop. At this stage the larva is, to all intents and purposes, a miniature replica of an adult axolotl.

Once hatched, the axolotl larvae must be given adequate

bottom surface area—the more space they have, the quicker they grow. If crowded they will often attack one another. As already mentioned, this cannibalistic behavior can be controlled to some degree by reducing the light level in the tank. As they grow, larvae should periodically be graded into groups of similar size.

Bottom Area Required by Growing Axolotls

Age	Bottom Surface area/cm body length
6 weeks old	10 cm^2
6-30 weeks old	30 cm^2
Adults	20 cm^2

For the first few days after hatching, the best food is *Artemia* (brine shrimp); alternatively, the smallest daphnia can be used. With the potential disease risks associated with wild-caught daphnia and the difficulties of home culture, the choice of brine shrimp is preferable. Brine shrimp hatcheries and eggs are available off the shelf from most pet stores. As the larvae grow they can next be fed on enchytraeid worms (white worms approximately 20-30 mm in length). Tubifex worms are also popular at this stage but should not be fed as the sole source of nutrients or liver problems can occur.

White worms and tubifex may be chopped up or cut with scissors as required to suit the size of the larvae. As soon as practicable, provide supplemental food such as earthworms (chopped as necessary), beef or liver. Liver is preferred for feeding young axolotls. Initially it will be necessary to hand-feed to encourage the larvae to take these "unnatural" foods. In time it is possible to condition them to feeding from the bottom.

An apparently successful diet for mass rearing of axolotl larvae is the use of daphnia for approximately three to four weeks; then, as the larvae become larger, introduce small mealworms or maggots. These can then be fed as a staple

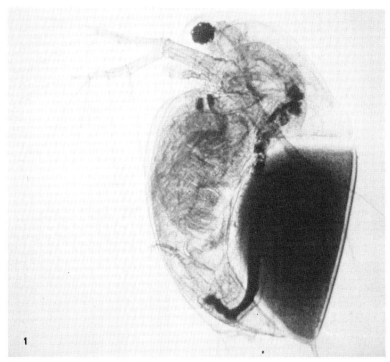

Both daphnia (1) and white worms (2) are good foods for larval and juvenile axolotls, but daphnia may carry parasites. Photo above by Geisler.

diet to all stock. If possible this diet should be supplemented with liver and heart.

GENETICS

There are a great number of mutant genes recorded from axolotls and producing a variety of effects, but the major aspect of genetics which is of interest to the axolotl keeper is the inheritance of color. The manner in which skin color is determined is a fascinating study. Color is dependent on an interaction among three types of specialized pigment cells called chromatophores situated in the dermal layer of the skin. These are melanophores (containing melanin, a black-brown pigment), iridophores (containing guanine and producing a shiny iridescence) and xanthophores (containing various yellow pigments).

Each cell of an axolotl, apart from those of the gonads, contains a total of 28 chromosomes in 14 pairs. One chromosome from each pair comes from each parent. The chromosomes are comprised of a series of genes; corresponding genes on pairs of chromosomes act together to control all aspects of development of the axolotl. The genes for color are inherited independently of one another and no linkage to other genes has been established.

The basic D/d system is the starting point. The color pattern determined by D involves development of large numbers of yellow xanthophores; in combination with melanophores they produce the dark olive-green background of the wild type of axolotl.

Iridophores are also found in the skin, but they are particularly prominent in the iris of the eye. In the homozygous recessive state (d/d) the white axolotl is produced. This has relatively small numbers of melanophores and xanthophores; as these white axolotls age even the few xanthophores and iridophores become obscured by the white skin. Patches of iridophores may remain visible around the gills.

1
2

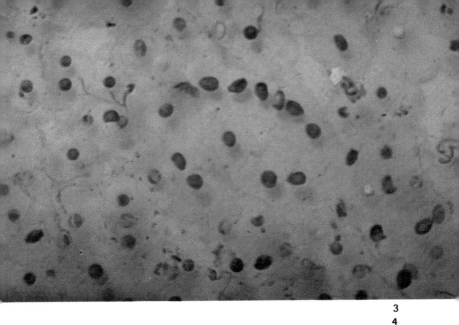

3
4

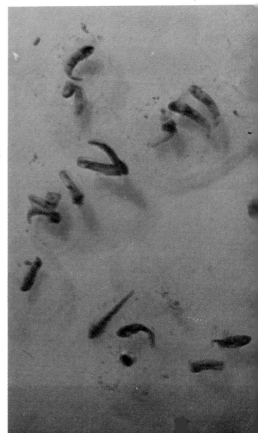

1) After proper conditioning, the pair spawns at night; a spermatophore can be seen between the forelegs. 2) The eggs are deposited over most surfaces in the tank. 3) A mass of eggs. Dead eggs (grayish) may fungus and should be removed. 4) Larvae near the end of the two-week incubation period and ready to hatch.

The albino axolotl results from a genetic combination which prevents the development of black pigmentation in the cells (melanophores), but it does not affect the other pigments in the skin namely the xanthophores and iridophores. Thus there are possibilities of having white, golden or even tan albino axolotls.

$$\left.\begin{array}{l} \text{D/D} \\ \text{D/d} \end{array}\right\} \text{dark} \qquad \left.\begin{array}{l} \text{M/M} \\ \text{M/m} \end{array}\right\} \begin{array}{l} \text{no} \\ \text{effect} \end{array} \qquad \left.\begin{array}{l} \text{A/A} \\ \text{Aa} \end{array}\right\} \begin{array}{l} \text{no} \\ \text{effect} \end{array} \qquad \left.\begin{array}{l} \text{AX/AX} \\ \text{AX/ax} \end{array}\right\} \begin{array}{l} \text{no} \\ \text{effect} \end{array}$$

d/d - white	m/m - melanoid	a/a - albino	ax/ax - axanthic (yellowless)
	$\underbrace{\qquad}$	$\underbrace{\qquad}$	$\underbrace{\qquad}$
	Acts on iridophores	Acts on melanophores	Acts on xanthophores

This D/d system is modified by subtraction of the component pigment cells. Each of the other genes in the homozygous recessive state results in the subtraction of the appropriate pigment, M on iridophores, A on melanophores and AX on xanthophores.

The albino axolotl results from the homozygous a/a combination, which prevents the development of melanophores but does not affect the xanthophores and iridophores. If combined with the d/d combination a white albino results. If, however, the albino genes are present in animals with D/D or D/d, then the xanthophores present lead to a yellow coloration. These animals have a striking gold appearance and should make rather attractive pets when they are more readily available.

Homozygosity for the gene m (*i.e.,* m/m) leads to an absence of iridophores and produces melanoid axolotls. These have a relative excess of melanophores and hence an overall charcoal gray color. In the white animals with d/d genes the melanoid condition shows itself only by the lack of iridophores in the iris producing a completely black iris. The melanoid condition seems to be connected also with spinal curvature (scoliosis). This seems to occur more commonly among melanoid animals than in normal dark axolotls.

The final variation on this color scheme is produced by the ax/ax combination, which produces the axanthic axolotl

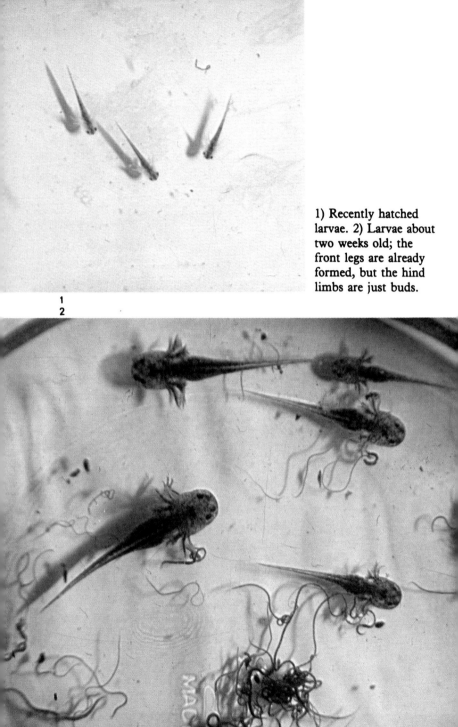

1) Recently hatched larvae. 2) Larvae about two weeks old; the front legs are already formed, but the hind limbs are just buds.

1
2

Of the several color varieties of axolotl, the harlequin (spotted) pattern is one of the most uncommon. However, it is also the most attractive.

1) Not all white axolotls are albinos; some have black eyes. Photo by L. E. Perkins. 2) An axolotl maintains its original color after metamorphosis.

72

with no visible xanthophores or iridophores; such animals look almost normal and would probably be mistaken for melanoid axolotls (m/m) due to the dull black iris resulting from an absence of iridophores.

Abnormalities of color are seen occasionally. A striking variation has great accumulations of melanophores leading to the formation of color spots. In some animals such spots are said to give rise to tumors; they become nodular and eventually lose some color and hemorrhage very easily. This is a great pity, since the color pattern is very attractive.

As axolotls become more popular on the pet market we are sure to see an increase in the gold axolotl and the spotted or harlequin color pattern.

Health
of
Axolotls

Two views of an axolotl showing
gross swelling of the lower jaw
and cloaca due to edema (build up
of fluids) caused by heart damage.

INHERITED PROBLEMS

A number of genetic disorders are catalogued for axolotls and there is a good deal of interest in such disorders in the laboratory field. They also provide a source of study for embryologists. The mutant genes that occur have been classified by Malacinski and Brothers in 1974 under the five different stages of development in which they exert their prime effect: (1) oogenesis, (2) early development, (3) organogenesis (organ development), (4) tissue and organ function and (5) adults.

The only problems of interest to pet keepers occur in groups 3 and 4. These include small or completely absent

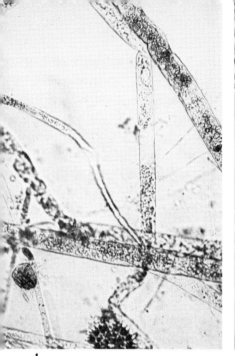
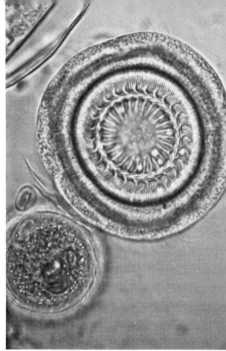

1) Hyphae of saprolegnia fungus like the one that attacks the eggs, larvae, and sometimes adults of axolotls. 2) Ventral view of the parasitic protozoan *Trichodina*, which can cause skin or gill damage in larvae. 3) Once an axolotl metamorphoses, it tends to be weaker and more susceptible to diseases; its longevity is also considerably curtailed.

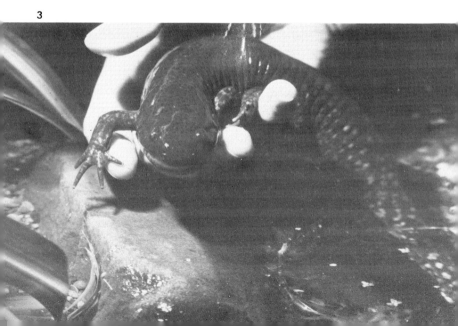

Enough cover is essential for the axolotls' sense of security. Here a variety of rocks and pots have been provided. The heater is used to maintain the temperature near 70° except when conditioning to spawn.

1

Live foods suitable for axolotls include almost anything edible, although the size of the food must be adjusted to the size of the animal. Wild-caught foods may carry parasites. 1) White worms. Photo by C.O. Masters. 2) Mealworms. 3) Tubifex worms. Photo by W. Tomey. 4) Adult brine shrimp. Photo by C.O. Masters.

2

3

4

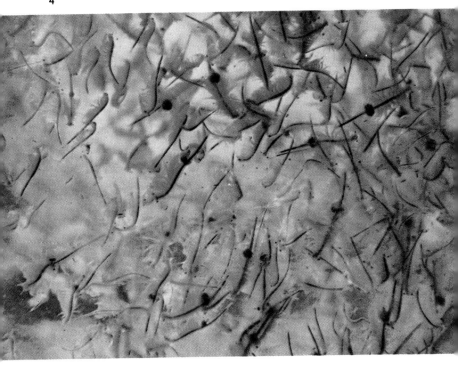

eyes, blood disorders such as anemia or cardiac ir-regularities and arrested or deformed limb development. Gills may be reduced, twisted or excessively fragile.

Genetic problems should be suspected if large numbers of larvae show developmental disorders. The remedy is ob-vious—avoid repetition of the particular mating and if possible, unless they are required for further research, destroy even the unaffected offspring as they are likely to be carrying the troublesome gene and therefore may spread its effect to future generations.

Body fluid disorders are fairly common in axolotls, such as accumulations of fluid in the abdomen (ascites) or under the skin, producing edema. There are genetic factors leading to this directly, but carriers of genes for anemia, heart irregularities and kidney insufficiency may also be more prone to such problems. There are other possible causes which will be discussed further on in this chapter.

BACTERIAL DISEASES

These may result in either local infections or generalized septicemias. The causative organisms vary, but by far the commonest are the aeromonads which cause "red leg."

This is basically a septicemic disease with organisms multiplying in the blood and causing a variety of signs. It usually results in heavy mortalities in groups of amphi-bians. Symptoms may range from local red areas to vomiting, anorexia (going off food), incoordination and sudden death. If this is suspected a veterinarian should be consulted with a view to instituting appropriate antibiotic treatment. Unfortunately the causative organisms of red leg are relatively resistant and difficult to treat.

Indiscriminate addition of antibiotics to the water should be strictly avoided. Adequate tissue levels of antibiotics are unlikely to be reached by this method except in the very small larvae with a relatively large surface area to volume ratio. The use of tetracyclines by this route may result in acute skin irritation. Antibiotic treatment of larger amphibians is normally carried out by stomach tube or by injection.

Another bacterial disease which may be encountered is tuberculosis, caused by organisms more closely related to those of fish tuberculosis than mammalian tuberculosis. Nodules may be found in the skin or internal organs, and again a variety of symptoms may be seen – from emaciation to generalized edema and gross swelling. There is unfortunately no guaranteed successful treatment, and affected animals should be destroyed.

When an outbreak of bacterial disease is encountered, it is important to give attention to the predisposing factors. These usually involve some form of stress, primarily poor water quality and rough handling. After treatment, an effort should be made to correct the underlying husbandry problem through better filtration or more frequent tank cleaning and generally better hygiene.

After bacterial problems have occurred in a tank it should be stripped and everything disinfected. For tuberculosis it is probably safer to dispose of all tank furnishings and start again. Any survivors should be viewed with suspicion, as they may be carriers and could infect any new stock.

FUNGAL INFECTIONS

All stages of development of axolotls may be affected by fungal problems. Dead eggs may act as a focus of infection from which parasitic fungi can spread to affect living eggs. Larvae of any age and adults may be affected with white tufts on the body, particularly around the head and cloaca. The major organism is saprolegnia, well known among aquarists as a widely occurring waterborne fungus. The factors leading to fungal infections are those also associated with bacterial diseases. These factors include poor water quality, rough handling leading to skin damage or excessively warm water.

1) When the temperature drops, undigested food may be regurgitated as a mucus-coated bolus. 2) Damage and resulting regeneration of the forelimb have here resulted in a double leg. 3) Minor wounds, such as this one of the caudal fin, usually heal well. 4) Cloacal prolapse associated with resorption of eggs without spawning; this condition often is fatal.

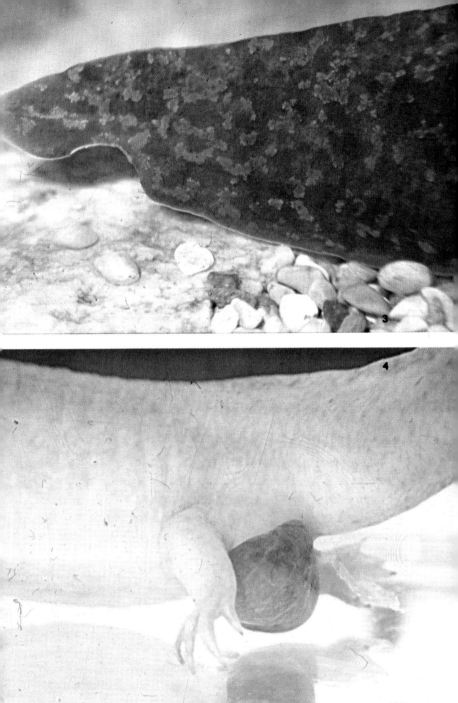

Treatment of fungal infections follows the same lines as it does in fish: improvement of conditions and treatment with chloramine, Mercurochrome or zinc-free malachite green. The former is probably the treatment of choice for the amateur. The animal should be placed in a 10 ppm solution and left there; a further dose of chloramine can be added after three to seven days if the infection is severe.

Any wounds may be treated if desired by swabbing with a 2% Mercurochrome solution; this can be applied to localized fungal infections. Mercurochrome can be used at a 2-4 ppm concentration as a three-day treatment for fungal infections; in severe cases this can be repeated, with an interval of a week in untreated water.

Care must be taken with any treatments used on amphibians because the skin, since it is involved in respiration, has a high absorptive capacity. Any new treatments should be carried out very carefully while watching for signs of toxicity. With this proviso, the principles of treatment and compounds used are very similar to those routinely applied by aquarists to fish problems.

PARASITIC INFESTATIONS

Ectoparasitic protozoa are said to be rare on amphibians. Although a number are recorded, they rarely cause problems. (When problems do occur they are usually associated with poor water conditions.) *Trichodina* species have caused problems on larvae. Problems of ectoparasitism should be suspected if excessive mucus is present on the skin and gills, or perhaps respiratory distress; this shows when animals hug the surface or the pump outflow. Treatments for this type of problem are Mercurochrome as described or a two-minute bath in 3% saline. These should be carried out in conjunction with improvement of the water conditions. A 1:1500 glacial acetic acid solution has been used as a 15-second dip for treatment of *Vorticella* infections.

Internal protozoa have been reported. *Glaucoma* (a ciliate

resembling *Tetrahymena,* a parasite causing problems in guppies) has been found in the brain and other tissues of axolotls. This report is in some doubt, however. Another writer reports coccidia in the liver as a major cause of death.

The finding of any amoeboid or ciliate organisms in the feces of sick axolotls should be considered carefully. At present very little is known about such diseases and it is probably safest to assume that they may be associated with the illness. In these cases it may be worthwhile consulting a veterinarian with a view to treatment of the axolotl with oral metronidazole.

Larger parasites such as helminths (roundworms and flatworms) may cause disease. If this is suspected, then the veterinarian may again be able to help, possibly using levamisole by injection or by dissolving it in the water for the treatment of roundworm infestations. Flatworms are likely to be very difficult to treat satisfactorily.

One major problem for anyone attempting treatment is dosage. Most of these drugs have only been used a very few times, certainly not often enough to be sure of their efficacy and safety. For this reason axolotl owners should be prepared for occasional failure or adverse reactions following treatment. As time progresses, laboratories working with axolotls may be able to provide more information on this subject.

MISCELLANEOUS PROBLEMS

A generalized edema and fluid build-up is sometimes seen in adult animals. This may be related to the swollen cloaca condition seen in some old animals. It is believed to be a result of kidney malfunction, perhaps due to an infection. It is possible that liver problems may also produce these symptoms. One possible factor leading to liver damage is the feeding of a high-fat diet such as one comprised mainly of oily seafish. This may arise particularly if

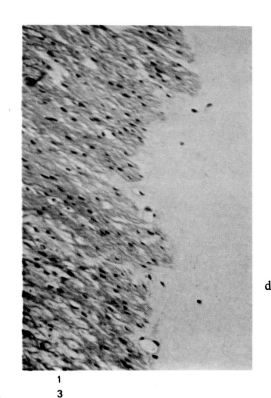

1

1) Slide through section of intestine of an axolotl with an undiagnosed infection. The epithelial cells have been virtually destroyed. 2) Nodules of tuberculosis in the liver of a fish. 3) Hyphae of the fungus *Saprolegnia*. Photo by D. McDaniel.

3

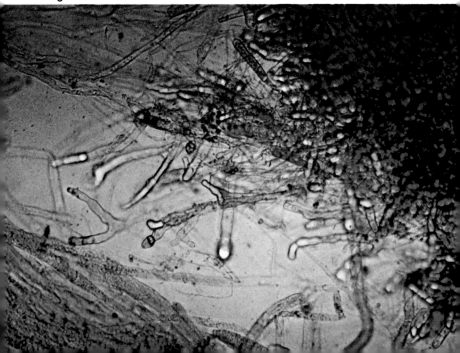

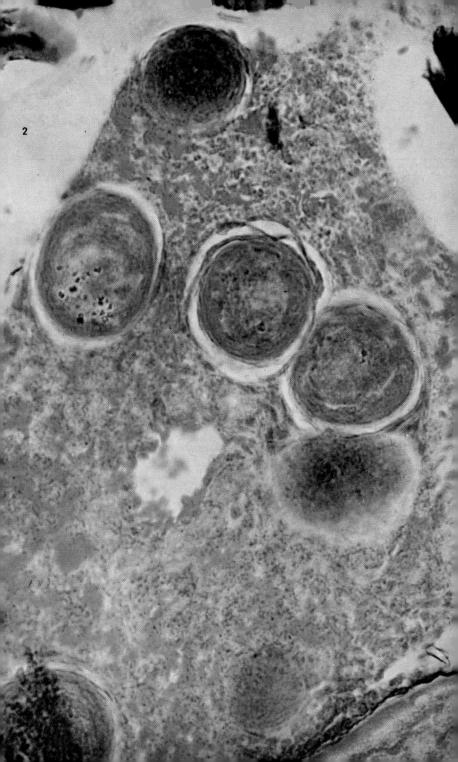

2

such fish have been stored for some time, thus allowing degradation of the vitamins and rancidity of the fat.

Feeding problems have occurred when larvae have been raised on a strict diet of white worms; these show hemorrhages in the feet, skin, stomach wall and peritoneal cavity, with death eventually occurring. Again this seems to be connected with high-fat levels in the liver. Some laboratories report difficulties when mealworms are used as a sole diet, although these seem to be adequate in practice.

Axolotls, in common with other aquatic amphibians, may swallow air at the surface and distend their stomachs, becoming tympanitic. This results in abnormal balance and swimming at the surface. Some of these resolve spontaneously; others may require gentle massage; a minority may need drainage by hypodermic puncture, a technique which should be left to the veterinarian.

Some axolotls, particularly if fed from the bottom, may accumulate sand or gravel in the stomach. This can lead to problems in swimming or continuous regurgitation every time food is taken. The condition can be confirmed by X-ray. Treatment is best carried out by several days' starvation followed by an oral dosage of mineral oil twice daily for three days or longer. If this is carried out in a bare tank, then its efficacy may be judged by checking feces passed by the axolotl.

Lastly, oversaturation of water with oxygen can result in skin and gill irritation, particularly in larvae. This may occur in tanks or in heavily planted aquaria receiving excess light—or even in natural conditions.

GENERAL RULES

As with any other animal, the secret of keeping axolotls healthy is basically good husbandry. A few simple rules may help.

1. Provide clean water conditions by adequate filtration or water changes and adequate oxygen levels.

A small plastic tub with an air supply can be used to keep and raise axolotls, but it must be kept clean through frequent siphoning and water changes. Dirty water and tank conditions promote diseases and parasites.

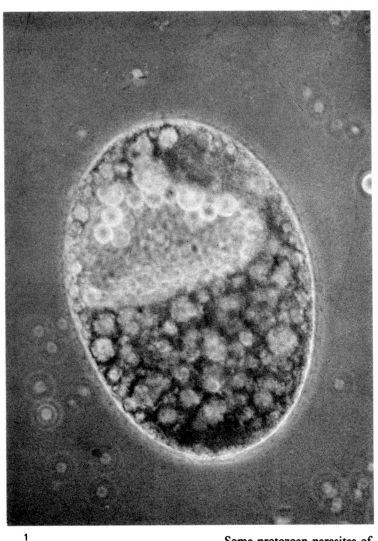

1

Some protozoan parasites of axolotls. 1) *Glaucoma* is very similar to the related *Tetrahymena* shown here. 2) *Vorticella* sometimes attaches to the skin or gills of axolotls and causes minor damage. 3) *Trichodina,* a highly specialized parasite sometimes found on larvae. Photos by Frickhinger.

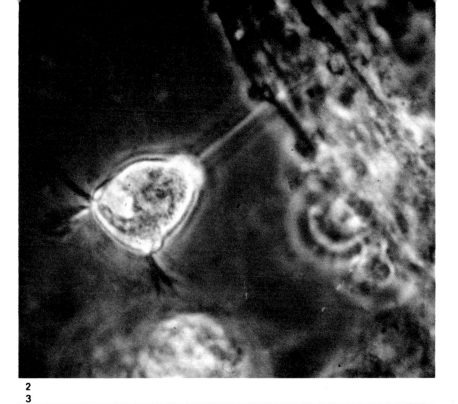

2

3

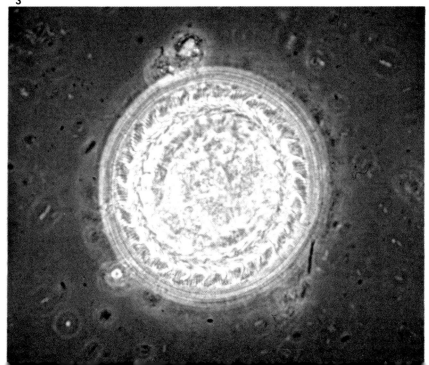

Healthy, well-kept axolotls can be attention-getters, but they must first get *your* complete attention and care. Photo by L.E. Perkins.

2. Provide an adequate balanced diet by giving a variety of foods, and avoid feeding any one food as the sole diet. If an imbalanced diet is being taken, then use a multivitamin supplement.
3. Carefully observe the normal animal to detect the abnormal.
4. Handle the axolotls carefully to avoid trauma and subsequent infection.
5. Keep records including diet, weight (if possible), water changes, diseases, treatments used and their efficacy, whether or not animals have bred and anything out of the ordinary.
6. Consult your veterinarian if you have a problem. He or she will be experienced in looking at disease problems, even if not specifically those of axolotls.

FURTHER READING

Elkan, E. and H. Reichenbach-Klinke, 1974. *Color Atlas of the Diseases of Fishes, Amphibians and Reptiles.* T.F.H. Publications, Inc.

Reichenbach-Klinke, H. and E. Elkan, 1965. *The Principal Diseases of Lower Vertebrates. Book 2. Diseases of Amphibians.* T.F.H. Publications, Inc.

Roberts, M. F., 1976. *All About Salamanders.* T.F.H. Publications, Inc.

Salthe, S. N. and J. S. Mecham, 1974. "Reproduction and Courtship Patterns," In: *Physiology of the Amphiba, Vol. 2.* (Edited by B. Lofts). Academic Press.

Smith, H. M., 1969. "The Mexican axolotl: Some misconceptions and problems," *Bioscience,* 19: 593-597.

Smith, H. M. and R. B. Smith, 1971. *Synopsis of the Herpetofauna of Mexico. Vol. 1. An Analysis of the Literature on the Mexican Axolotl.* Eric Lundberg, Augusta, W. Va.

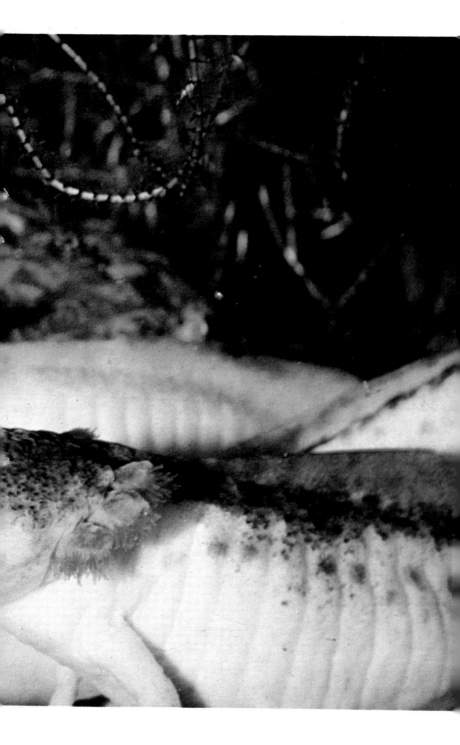

AXOLOTLS